Let's Share

MY FIRST MANNERS

Written by Constance Allen

Illustrated by Maggie Swanson

Published by Phoenix International Publications, Inc.
8501 West Higgins Road, Suite 300, Chicago, Illinois 60631
Lower Ground Floor, 59 Gloucester Place, London W1U 8JJ

www.pikidsmedia.com

p i kids is a trademark of Phoenix International Publications, Inc., and is registered in the United States.

8 7 6 5 4 3 2

ISBN: 978-1-4127-6783-5

 phoenix international publications, inc.

What should the monster do?

Give you a hint: It rhymes with "Try to be **fair!**"

Share! Especially when you've got two!

What should the monster do?

Give you a hint: It rhymes with
"Give up your **chair**!"

Share! It's the polite thing to do!

What should the monster do?

Give you a hint: It rhymes with
"He has an extra **pear**."

Share! It's the nice thing to do!

What should the monster do?

Give you a hint: It rhymes with
"She's got a **spare**."

Share! Games are more fun
when they're played by two!

Share! It's the thoughtful thing to do!

What should the monster do?

What do the monsters do?

You guessed it! **Share!**